Liar!

by

Pete Johnson

Illustrated by Julia Page

First published in 2008 in Great Britain by
Barrington Stoke Ltd
18 Walker St, Edinburgh, EH3 7LP

www.barringtonstoke.co.uk

ISBN: 978-1-84299-553-2

Printed in Great Britain by Bell & Bain Ltd

A Note from the Author

My best mates and I were always messing around at school.

We'd play little tricks on each other – and try and get our friends to smile when we weren't meant to. So when the headmaster was angry and shouting at us, one of my friends would tickle me and make me giggle!

But that was all right, it was just a bit of fun. One day, though, a window was smashed. And someone tried to put the blame on me. Someone I'd thought was a really good mate.

This really messed up our friendship. I never forgot that moment. I still haven't.

And once you fall out with best mates … it's very easy to start hating them.

In fact, a good friend can turn into your worst enemy really fast.

And then … but I think I've told you all you need to know for now.

Read on, if you want to know more.

Contents

Chapter 1

A Narrow Escape

I didn't mean to push Dave in front of that car. Of course I didn't. He was my best mate.

He and I were walking home from school, glad the day was over. Every teacher had been in a bad mood, telling you off for nothing.

Then someone called out: "Hi, Ryan!" I turned round. This girl, who had a job in the corner shop, was smiling at me. She had long, dark hair and a very cute smile.

I said, "Hi." She went back into the shop. And then I went bright red. Well, it was a bit of a shock. I didn't even know she knew my name. She was also years older than me.

Then Dave began jumping about and yelling, and I punched him, but in a playful way. Then we had this little fight right in

the middle of the road. I knocked Dave over.

But we were laughing the whole time.

Then suddenly, a car came racing along the road. I tried to pull Dave up from the ground. But the car was going too fast.

I let out a cry of horror. The driver hit the brakes. The car swerved and skidded to a stop. I helped Dave to his feet. He was shaking. So was I.

The driver jumped out of his car. He was white with anger. "What do you think you're doing? You could have been killed." I didn't argue with him. Dave and I had been stupid, all right.

But the driver just went on yelling at us. And in the end Dave laughed. He wasn't being rude. He was laughing with relief.

But the driver didn't see that. "You want locking up," he yelled at Dave. "You're out of control." Then he marched off to the shops. Dave and I slipped away.

"Talk about a narrow escape," he said.

"Yeah, I really hoped I'd got rid of you," I told him.

Dave laughed. He and I were always messing about, making fun of each other. Dave had only moved here a few months ago. But already we were good mates.

We reached Dave's house. He said to me, "That driver was hopping mad, wasn't he?"

"Can't really blame him," I said. "Still, it's all over now."

But it wasn't at all.

Chapter 2

A Big Lie

Later that evening the phone rang. Dad was talking to someone for ages. I was in my bedroom, doing my homework. So I did hear what Dad was saying. But I didn't think it could have anything to do with me.

Then I heard Dad say: "I'm very, very sorry," and he put the phone down. He and Mum talked together in shocked voices for a moment. Then they came pounding up the stairs. Dad pushed my door open.

"You're meant to knock," I began. But I saw Dad was glaring at me. Mum was looking very cross too.

"What's wrong?" I asked.

"I've just been talking to David's father," he said. "He's very angry with you."

"What!" I cried.

"He says you pushed David into the road and threw him under a car – all because he made a little joke about a girl."

"No, no," I began. "Dave and I were just having a laugh."

"That's not what David says," said my dad. "He says you attacked him for no reason. He says you're always picking on him."

"Did you push David into the road?" asked Mum.

"Well, yes," I said.

"We're so ashamed of you," cried Dad. "And no pocket money for two weeks."

I opened my mouth to argue.

"And if you say just one more word," cried Dad, "you won't get any pocket money for a month."

When my dad gets that angry, it's best just to leave him alone. So I tried ringing Dave. But his mobile was switched off. This was very odd. And it stayed switched off for the rest of the evening.

Was Dave hiding from me? And why had he said I'd picked on him?

****

I waited at school for him next morning. He saw me and gave an odd little smile.

"What's going on?" I shouted. "Why did you tell your dad I pushed you into the road?"

"I know, I'm sorry about that," said Dave. "But I had to do it. That driver came round to my house last night."

"How did he find out your name?" I asked.

"He asked someone in the shops," said Dave.

"Well, he never wanted to find out my name," I said. "But then, I didn't laugh at him, like you."

15

"Yeah, well never mind that," said Dave. "The thing is, he moaned on and on about me to my dad. And you know how mad my dad can get. He can stay angry for weeks."

"So can mine," I told him.

"But my dad does crazy things like ..." Dave spoke in a low voice, "shut me up in the dark cupboard under the stairs all night."

I smiled. "So when did your dad do that?"

"I didn't say he had done it," cried Dave. "But he could do it. That's why I had to pretend it was all your fault."

"Well thanks a bunch for that," I said.

"Why? It doesn't matter, does it?" asked Dave. "And you've saved me – your best mate – from a night of torture under the stairs."

"While I've got no pocket money for two weeks. And my mum and dad keep giving me evil looks ..."

"They'll have forgotten it by tonight," Dave said.

"But why should I take the blame?" I said. "It was all your fault."

"It wasn't *all* my fault," said Dave.

"Yes it was," I told him. "That driver was cooling off until you started laughing at him. That's what sent him wild."

"Look, bruv," said Dave. "That driver was a weird saddo and I'm sick of talking about him. Let's just forget it."

18

But I couldn't do that. Inside I was still very angry. Dave had no right to make up lies about me.

Suddenly I wanted to get my own back on Dave. And that afternoon, I got my chance.

Chapter 3

I am in Big Trouble

The last lesson of the day was English.
Mr Giles was reading to us from a book.
Then he suddenly said: "Now I want someone
else to read to the class." Everyone just
hates doing that. It's so shame making. And
no one put up their hand.

Then I called out, "Dave will do it."

"Shut up," he hissed.

But I didn't. I shouted. "Dave is a bit shy, sir. But he'd just love to read to the class."

"Well done, Dave," said Mr Giles. "Off you go."

Dave's face was bright red now. And he stumbled over every word. It was terrible. The whole class was laughing at him. Even Mr Giles couldn't help smiling.

Dave stared at me as if I was something dirty he'd stepped on. "Why did you do that?" he asked me.

"It was only a joke," I told him.

"Well, I'm not laughing," said Dave. He looked hurt, as well as very angry.

When school finished, Dave didn't wait for me. He went off on his own – in a sulk. But what did I care?

At home, Mum and Dad were still in a bad mood with me. They really thought I'd pushed Dave into the road for no reason.

"You're in big trouble," said Zoe, my older sister. She knew what had been going on. But she said: "Best friends always let you down. You can't trust one of them. I should know."

Yesterday I would have said she was wrong. Now I wasn't so sure.

Next morning I rode my bike to school. Cycling is a big hobby of mine. But Dave hasn't even got a decent bike. That's why most days I don't go to school on mine, so I can walk with him.

My dad watched me leave. He suddenly smiled at me. That was a shock. But he loves cycling too. "I'm pleased you've remembered to wear your cycling helmet," he said. Even though I'm fifteen, he's still very strict about things like that.

At school a group of boys stood around admiring my bike. Then someone asked if he could ride around on it.

It was all going so well until my cycling helmet vanished. No one knew where it had gone. I looked everywhere. And when I got home Dad stormed out of the house. "What are you doing riding about without your helmet?"

"I can't find it," I said. "I think it's been stolen."

Dad shook his head. He was very angry. He didn't believe me. And next day my cycling helmet was back again. I found it by my locker. But it had a bad dent.

I was so shocked I just stared at it. Who would do something so nasty and stupid?

And then I saw Dave.

He was standing watching me. "See what someone has done," I said. "I can't believe it."

Dave didn't say a word but he looked away.

"You don't know anything about this, do you?"

"Of course not," said Dave. He sounded angry. But he still wasn't looking at me.

He really did look as if he'd done it.

"Are you sure it wasn't you?" I said.

He laughed a weird laugh which didn't sound like Dave at all.

Then, without another word he marched away.

Chapter 4

Fight

Two days later it was Dave's birthday. He came into school looking very pleased with himself. Then I saw why.

His dad had bought him the very latest mobile phone. Soon everyone was admiring it – except me. I was too angry.

For my dad was stopping my pocket money for another two weeks. This was because he'd seen me on my bike, without a helmet. I was sure Dave had taken it and dented it, making trouble for me again. Yet, here he was, showing off his brilliant new phone.

Hate for Dave filled me and made my heart pound. Then later, I saw his mobile hidden under his desk. He didn't want the teacher to see it, as we're not allowed to bring phones to school.

Suddenly, I grabbed the mobile phone and walked quickly away with it. I didn't mean to steal it. I just thought, *I'll hide it for a while – and get back at Dave.*

Dave was as mad as a snake when he found his mobile was missing. I was pleased. I wanted to spoil his birthday. He rushed up to me. "OK, where is it?"

"I don't know what you're talking about," I said. I could lie just as well as him.

Dave stared at me with wild eyes. "Give it back to me," he hissed.

"Sorry, can't help you," I told him.

Suddenly I felt Dave's fist crash on to my chin. At once I tried to punch him back. We'd had lots of pretend fights before. But this was different. We were both crazy with rage.

A group of boys gathered round yelling: "Fight! Fight!"

But a teacher came striding towards us. "Stop this at once," he yelled. And he gave us both a double detention.

"You'd better give me my mobile back," said Dave.

"Oh, I'm shaking with fear," I said and smiled.

Then that night Dave sent me an e-mail. "If you don't return my mobile tomorrow, I'll get my dad to call the police. And you'll be in big, big trouble."

Chapter 5

The Shock of My Life

Later I sat in my bedroom staring at Dave's mobile. What was I going to do now? I'd never meant to steal it. I just wanted to get back at Dave.

Suddenly my bedroom door opened. I jumped in alarm, afraid it was my mum or dad. They'd want to know why I had Dave's mobile. And what could I tell them?

But it was Zoe. She spotted the mobile at once. She let out a low whistle as she picked it up. "Now, that is class," she said.

"I took it today," I said. "I must have been mad."

I told her the whole story. She sat on the edge of my bed, and listened to me.

For once she didn't say a word. Then she said, "You've got to somehow sneak the phone back to Dave." She leaned forward. "I know, go into school early tomorrow and leave it by the lockers. Then he'll find it – and he can't prove you took it." She got up. "And you must get a new best mate."

"It's not that easy," I replied.

"Oh, yes it is," she said. "I'm always changing mine."

I didn't sleep very well that night. And next morning I slipped out of the house very early. No one seemed to be at school at all – though the care-taker might have been about somewhere. It was weird seeing the school so still and silent.

I got to the lockers as fast as I could. This was where I planned to leave Dave's phone. But then I got the shock of my life. Someone was already there. And he was smashing open the lockers. Then I watched him hurl some of the stuff from the lockers

into his pockets. The rest he threw on to the floor. I had to do something.

I ran towards him. The boy spun round. I'd never seen him before. I was sure he didn't go to my school.

"Hey, what do you think you're doing?" I cried. A silly thing to ask – as it was very clear what he was doing. Then I added, "Put all the stuff back now!"

The boy didn't reply. He just darted off. I went racing after him. "Stop, thief," I yelled. I hoped the care-taker might hear me.

But it was someone else who came rushing forward and grabbed hold of the boy. Dave.

Chapter 6
The Truth

Together, Dave and I dragged the boy to the care-taker's office. As we pulled him along, things he'd stolen kept dropping out of his pocket.

"You *have* been busy," Dave said to him.

The care-taker nearly fell over with shock when he saw us. But he acted fast, taking the boy to the Headmaster's office.

"What about that?" said Dave, punching the air.

"Yeah, we've caught a burglar," I yelled.

We were so excited. The care-taker rushed back. He told us the boy had broken into the school before. "You did very well catching him," he said. Then he turned to Dave. "Wasn't your mobile phone stolen yesterday?"

I felt myself freeze.

But Dave said, "No, it turned up after all. I'd just lost it."

After the care-taker had gone, I asked, "Why did you say that?"

Dave shrugged. "You have got it, haven't you?"

Without another word I pulled the mobile out of my pocket. I said, "You came into school early to catch me putting it back?"

Dave nodded.

Then he turned away and said softly. "It was me who took your cycling helmet and dented it. And I shouldn't have lied to my dad."

"No you shouldn't ..." I began. But then I stopped and said. "It all seems to have gone mad in the last few days ..."

"And now it all just seems so stupid," said Dave.

It was then we both remembered something. We were mates. Good mates. And Zoe was wrong; you can't just go off and find another best friend. They're special.

Of course mates will drive you mad sometimes. But you can't let that take you over – as we had done.

Dave grinned at me. "I've missed your ugly mug."

"I might even have missed yours," I said.

And we walked off together.

Barrington Stoke would like to thank all its readers for commenting on the manuscript before publication and in particular:

Kanesha Agard
Jordan Angel
Debbie Ashenden
Alex B.
Billy Barrett
Charlotte Brookes
Jamie Brown
Judy Carter-Brown
Nilli Jubayra Choudhury
Tyrone Cooper
Nick Creighton
Leanne-Marie Cross
Harry Curtis
Rebecca Davis
Crystal Downes
Jessica Goode
Deanna Harvey
Abigail Hemmings

Andrew Hill
Chelsea Hutin
Kelly Hyman
Lauren Killick
Roxanne Mitchell
Tom Nabulsi
Emma Norman
Sean Pritchard
Reese Rushmer
Natalie Salter
Gareth Slims-Brassett
Matthew Sullivan
Matthew Thomas
Steven Thompson
Chlöe Tumbu
Holly Weymoth
Aaron Worth

Become a Consultant!

Would you like to give us feedback on our titles before they are published? Contact us at the email address below – we'd love to hear from you!

info@barringtonstoke.co.uk
www.barringtonstoke.co.uk

Great reads – no problem!

Barrington Stoke books are:

Great stories – from thrillers to comedy to horror, and all by the best writers around!

No hassle – fast reads with no boring bits, and a story that doesn't let go of you till the last page.

Short – the perfect size for a fast, fun read.

We use our own font and paper to make it easier to read our books. And we ask teenagers like you, who want a no-hassle read, to check every book before it's published.

That way, we know for sure that every Barrington Stoke book is a great read for everyone.

Check out www.barringtonstoke.co.uk for more info about Barrington Stoke and our books!

More gr8reads from Barrington Stoke

**Don't Call Us
by
Pat Thomson**

The gang want Jack to help them steal some games consoles.
They will get him if he says no.
What can he do?

**Two Words
by
Tanya Landman**

Two friends.
A hiking trip.
A mistake that changes everything.

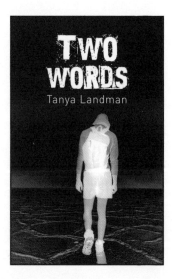

You can order these books directly from our website at
www.barringtonstoke.co.uk

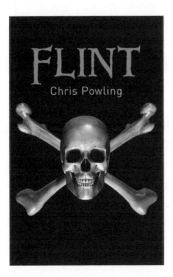

**Flint
by
Chris Powling**

Captain Flint.
Pirate. Thief. Killer
And Edmund is his
prisoner. Can he survive
– or will Flint bury him
with the treasure?

**Mind-Set
by
Joanna Kenrick**

Mark and Shaleem are
best mates.
But the bombs change
everything.
Will Mark stand up for
Shaleem when it
matters?

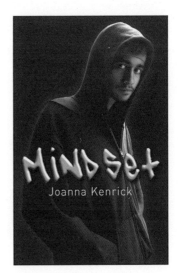

You can order these books directly from our website at
www.barringtonstoke.co.uk